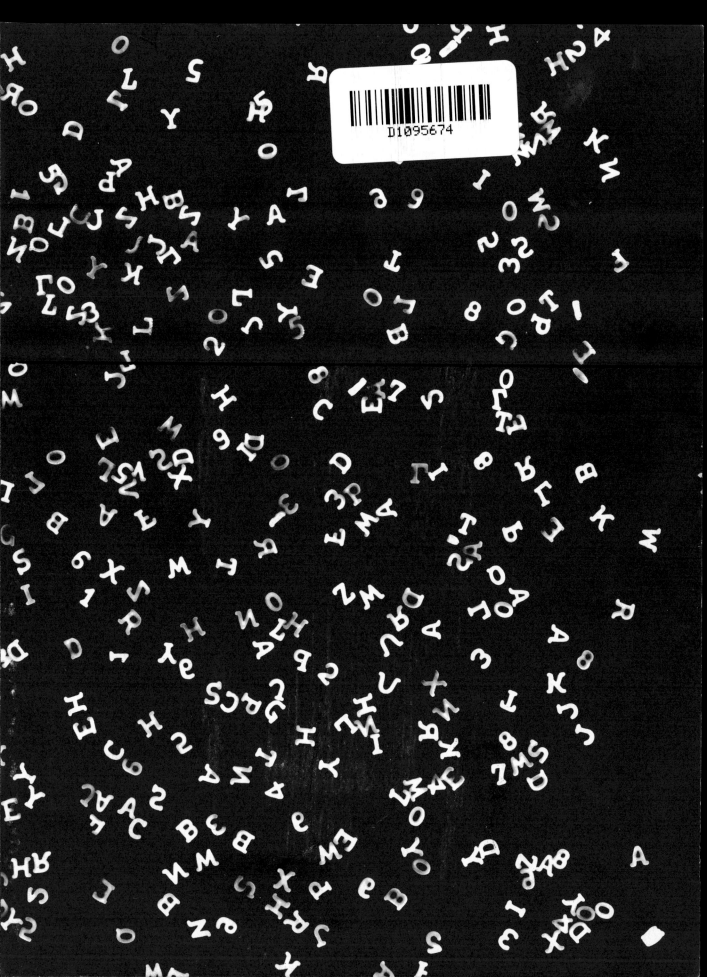

D1095674

Shapes

TANA HOBAN
and Things

MACMILLAN PUBLISHING CO., INC.
New York
COLLIER MACMILLAN PUBLISHERS
London

Macmillan Publishing Co., Inc.,
866 Third Avenue, New York, N.Y. 10022
Collier-Macmillan Canada Ltd.

Library of Congress Catalog Card Number: 70–102965

10 9 8 7 6 5 4 3

For Eddie and Miela

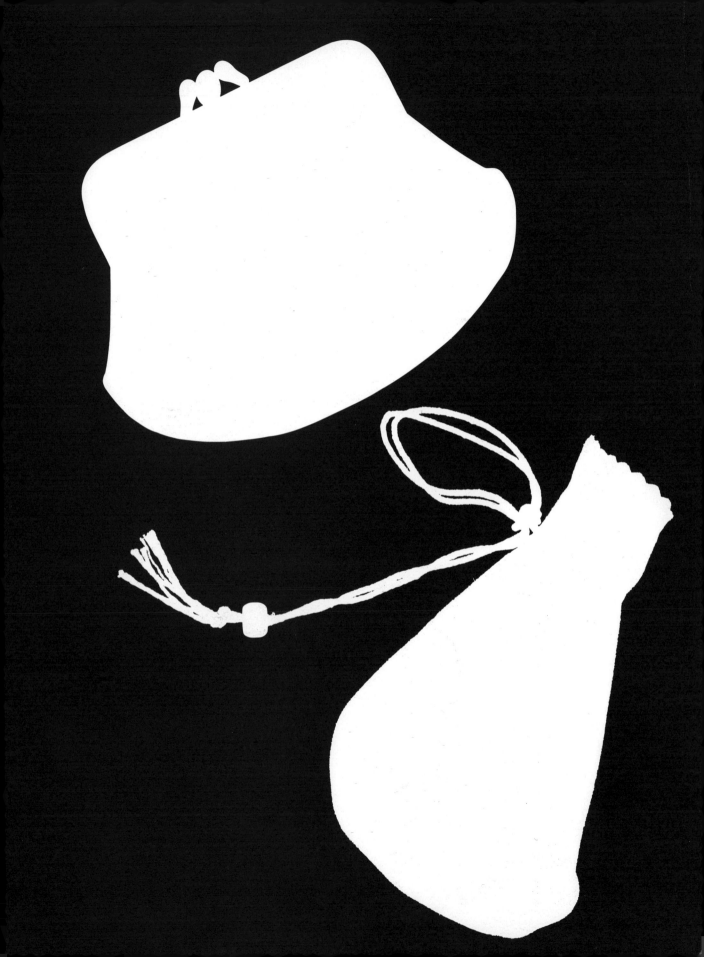

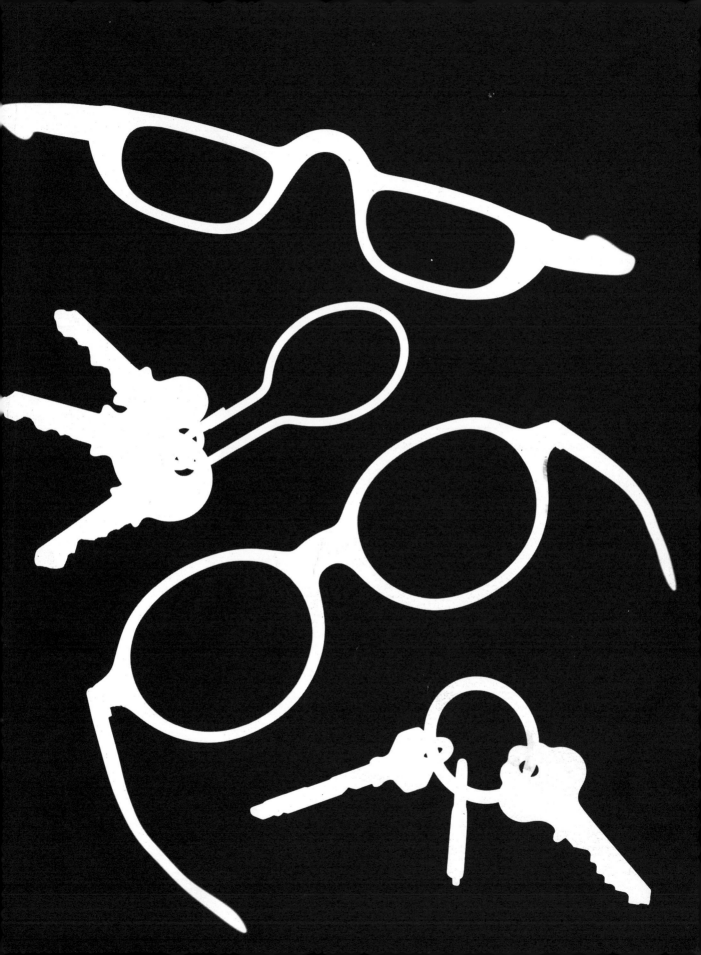

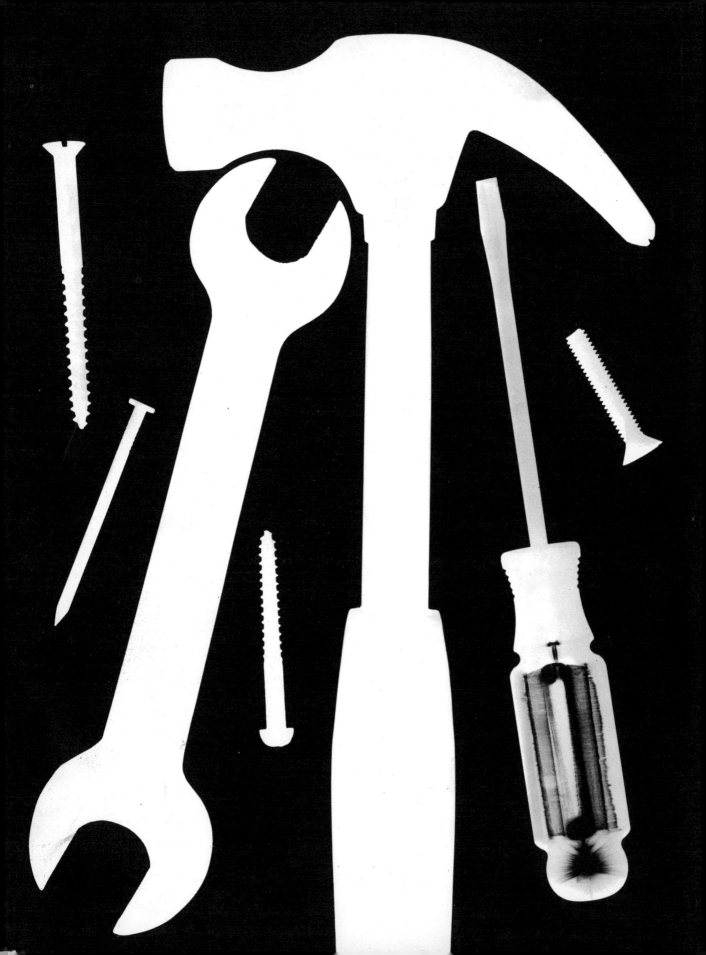

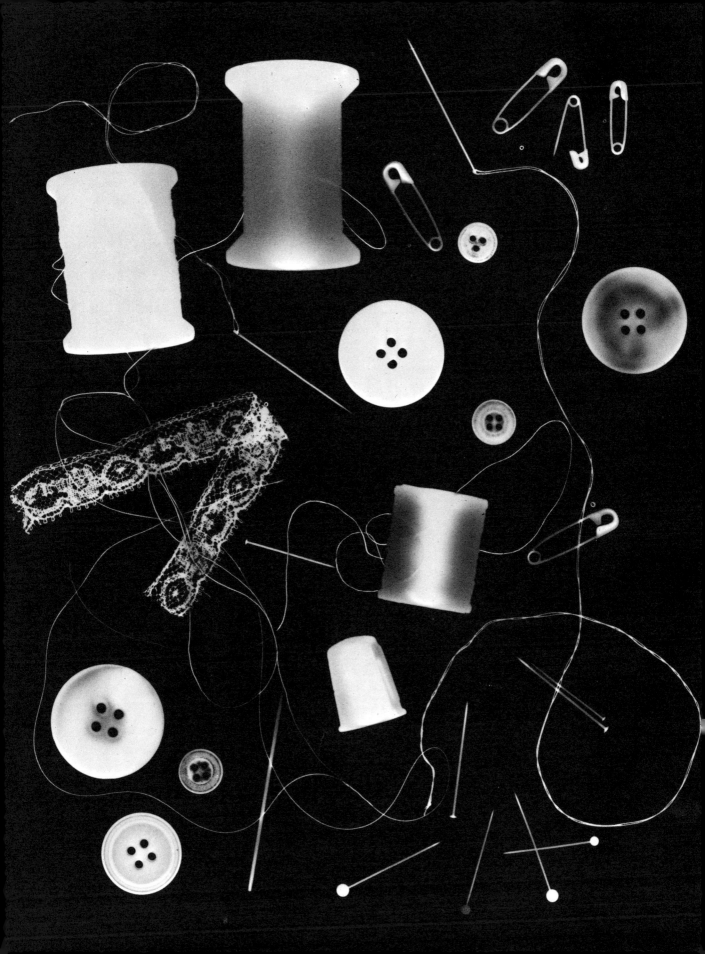

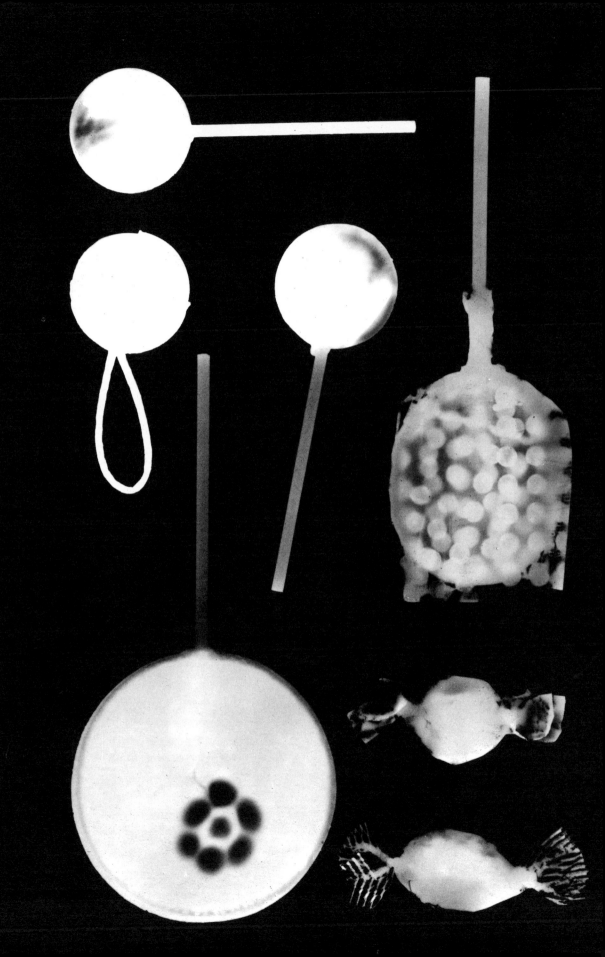

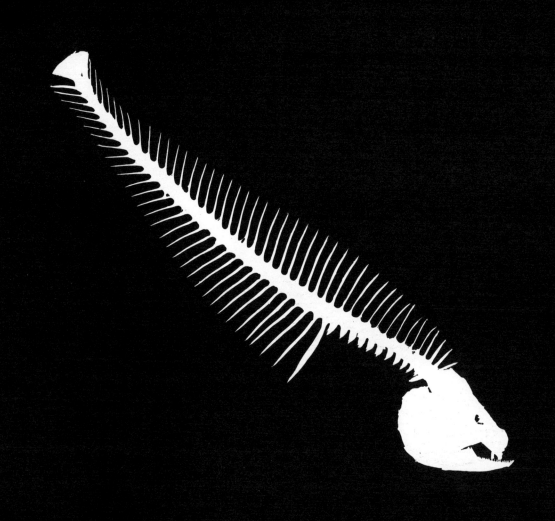